Fun

written by

Karl Newson

illustrated by

Lucy Fleming

For the Pencil Wobblers - KN
For my Nan - LF

The Crumbs are a big family...

...a REALLY big family.

There's Pa,

Ma

and Grandpa Plum.

Fee

and Fi

and Fo

and... Fum?
Has anyone seen
the smallest Crumb?

Where did he go? Where could he be?
Is he playing house with the little pigs three?"

"Chinny-chin-chin!"

said Grandpa Plum, and off they went to search for Fum.

Down
the
lane
and
past
the
store.

KNOCK!

KNOCK!

KNOCK!

on the Little Pigs' door.

"Hello down there!" said Grandpa Plum,
"Have you seen the smallest Crumb?"

One pig oinked, "He could be hiding...
In the woods with Little Red Riding."

"Ah, Miss Hood!" said Big Pa Crumb, and off they went to search for Fum...

Through the trees

and up the track,

all the way to Grandma's shack.

"Hello down there!" said Grandpa Plum,
"Have you seen the smallest Crumb?"

But Big Bad Wolf could smell his socks,
"He's gone to play with Goldilocks!"

"Gobbling porridge!"
said Ma Crumb,
and off they went to search for Fum...

"Into the thicket and over the bridge,
to the house upon the ridge."

"Hello down there!" said Grandpa Plum,

"Have you seen the smallest Crumb?"

"**No,**
but," Little Bear yelled, "I know the place!"
And one by one, they all took chase.

OH! Where could he be?

Where did he go?

DOESN'T ANYBODY

KNOW?!

"Hello up there!"
a little voice said.

"Have you looked
above your head?"

"Oh!"

"Oh!"

"Oh!"

"Oh!"

"Hello Fum!" said Grandpa Plum.
At last they'd found the smallest Crumb.

You see, Fum wasn't lost at all.
He's been right here...

he's just small.

The woods filled up with songs and laughter,
and all lived happily ever after.

The End

Fum
An original concept by author Karl Newson
Text © Karl Newson

Illustrations © Lucy Fleming

The rights of the author and illustrator have been asserted.

Published by MAVERICK ARTS PUBLISHING LTD
Studio 3a, City Business Centre, 6 Brighton Road,
Horsham, West Sussex, RH13 5BB +44 (0) 1403 256941
© Maverick Arts Publishing Limited March 2017

A CIP catalogue record for this book is available at the British Library.

Maverick
arts publishing

www.maverickbooks.co.uk

ISBN: 978-1-84886-243-2